Kids Learn!

Getting Ready for

5th Grade

Publishing Credits

Rachelle Cracchiolo, M.S.Ed., *Publisher*
Aubrie Nielsen, M.S.Ed., *EVP of Content Development*
Emily R. Smith, M.A.Ed., *VP of Content Development*
Véronique Bos, *Creative Director*
Robin Erickson, *Art Director*
Caroline Gasca, M.S.Ed., *Senior Content Manager*
Lynette Ordoñez, *Content Specialist*
Jill Malcolm, *Multimedia Specialist*

Image Credits

All images Shutterstock and/or iStock

Standards

5482 Argosy Avenue
Huntington Beach, CA 92649-1039
www.tcmpub.com
ISBN 978-1-0876-6285-5
© 2022 Teacher Created Materials
Printed in Malaysia. THU001.8400

Table of Contents

Welcome Letter

Dear Family,

Kids Learn! Getting Ready for 5th Grade was designed to help your child solidify the concepts learned in fourth grade and prepare for the year ahead. The engaging activities are based on today's standards and provide practice with essential reading, writing, and math skills for the upcoming grade level. This book will help your child GET READY for fifth grade! Keep these tips in mind as you work with your child:

◆ Have your child complete one or two pages each time they work, rather than an entire week's worth of activities at one time.

◆ Keep all practice sessions with your child positive and constructive. If your child gets frustrated, set the book aside and find another time to practice.

◆ Help your child with instructions, if necessary. If your child is having difficulty understanding what to do, work through some of the problems together.

◆ Encourage your child to creatively share their thoughts and feelings on the My Journal pages.

Enjoy spending time with your child. Fifth grade will be here before you know it!

What Does Your Rising Fifth Grader Need to Know?

1 Identify morals and themes in various types of texts.

2 Identify and describe conflict, climax, resolution, and character development in stories.

3 Understand parts of words, including root words, prefixes, and suffixes.

4 Add and subtract fractions and decimals to hundredths.

5 Divide large numbers by multi-digit numbers using long division.

6 Understand coordinate planes and ordered pairs.

7 Know about bacteria and other major domains of life.

8 Understand solids, liquids, and other states of matter.

9 Know about the history of the United States, including the 13 colonies, the American Revolution, and the Civil War.

10 Learn about the states in the United States and their capitals.

Things to Do as a Family

General Skills

◆ Make sure your child gets plenty of sleep. Children this age need 9–11 hours of sleep each night. Establish bedtime routines that involve relaxing activities, such as taking a warm shower or reading.

◆ Help your child become organized and responsible. Have places for your child to keep important things. Take time to set up a schedule together. Use a timer to keep track of time spent on different activities.

Reading Skills

◆ Set a reading time for the entire family at least every other day. You can read aloud or read silently. Help your child choose books that are at a comfortable reading level and that are interested to them.

◆ After reading, be sure to talk to your child about what they have read. Ask questions about the characters, the plot, and the setting. Encourage your child to share details from the books.

Things to Do as a Family *(cont.)*

Writing Skills

◆ Encourage your child to write emails, texts, or letters to friends and family members who live near and far.

◆ Have your child create an online blog or keep a diary or journal about activities they are doing during time off from school.

Mathematics Skills

◆ Have your child estimate measurements while out in the community. For example: "This sidewalk is about 30 inches wide. About how wide do you think the driveway is?"

◆ Involve your child in cooking dinner. This is a great way to teach about fractions as well as liquid and dry units of measure.

Games to Play Together

Yes/No
Critical-Thinking Questions

Take any game that is traditionally a guessing game (Guess My Number) and make it a yes/no question game. You say, "I'm thinking of a number from 1 to 200." Children have to ask you yes/no questions with mathematically accurate vocabulary. They might say, "Is the number prime?" If a child asks a question without using mathematical vocabulary, don't answer the question. And definitely don't answer if anyone just takes guesses!

ABC Categories

Think of a category and name an object from that category for every letter of the alphabet. Make it more challenging by choosing more difficult categories or by having every person name an example for every letter. Popular categories are movies, characters from books, or things seen on vacation.

Favorites

Think of a topic, and then everyone names their favorite examples of that topic. Someone might say, "Movies." Everyone would name their favorite movies. Allowing different people to think of the category each time helps keep the game interesting for everyone. It's fascinating to children that everyone enjoys such different things.

Books to Read Together

Out of My Mind by Sharon M. Draper

Reading about this young girl with cerebral palsy will give your child a new perspective on the challenges he or she faces. Your child will be cheering the protagonist on as she discovers how to show her voice to those adults and children who can't see past her special needs.

Stef Soto, Taco Queen by Jennifer Torres

It's no fun being known as the "Taco Queen" at school. Seventh-grader Stef Soto wants her dad to stop picking her up in the family's taco truck and to get a normal job. What will make her change her mind?

When the Mountain Meets the Moon by Grace Lin

This book blends Chinese folk tales and mythology into a wonderful story. The story's themes include friendship, adventure, and hope. The book is a wonderful way to look back in history and learn about a culture that may be very different from your own.

Bud, Not Buddy by Christopher Paul Curtis

In this touching novel, Bud is searching for his father after the death of his mother. He begins the journey on his own, but he meets very interesting and engaging characters along the way. His earnest journey is an adventure you'll never forget.

Family Science Experiment

Science experiments can be great learning opportunities for children and fun ways for families to spend time together. Try this activity with the whole family. Or visit your local science museum's website for more great activity ideas.

Build a Parachute

Have your family work together to create a parachute for a toy. Experiment with different materials, folds, and shapes to create the best parachute possible. Secure the parachute to a small toy with string or tape to test your family's designs.

Suggested Materials

- glue
- handkerchief
- plastic bags
- small toy
- string
- tape
- tissues

Social-Emotional Development

Children's social-emotional development is just as important as their academics. Healthy social-emotional development helps students feel well-adjusted, prepares them to handle change and conflict, and allows them to understand their own emotions. Use the following suggestions to help your child learn about themselves.

Peer Pressure

Your child has likely experienced some sort of peer pressure. Talk to your child about the kinds of things they might be pressured to do. Discuss what they can do in those situations, such as walking away, changing the subject, or firmly but politely saying *no*. You may wish to role-play some of these situations with your child to help prepare them.

Knowing Your Triggers

Triggers are events that create intense emotional reactions. We all have triggers, and they vary from person to person. Some common triggers are unfair treatment, things being taken away, and being called unkind names. Knowing your own triggers and your child's can help your family deal with these intense emotions. Talk to your child about their triggers and what they can do to anticipate their emotions or calm down.

I-Messages

Teach your child to use I-messages. A good I-message doesn't blame, says how the person is feeling, and tells the other person how they could do things differently. For example, imagine a child is upset because their teacher gave them a bad grade on something they worked very hard to do. A less helpful message might sound like, "You gave me a bad grade. You don't like me!" But an I-message might sound like, "I'm sad that I got this grade. I worked very hard. I want to understand why I got this grade."

Social-Emotional Development *(cont.)*

Stress Management

As children get older, learning how to manage stress becomes more and more important. Children may need to balance their increasingly difficult schoolwork with sports, music, clubs, or other activities. Help your child stay organized so that they know when assignments are due and can plan accordingly. Try to allow your child some unstructured time each day to relax and unwind. Talk to your child about things they can do when they feel stressed, such as deep breathing or journaling.

Using Technology Safely

In our increasingly digital world, children use more types of technology younger and younger. Talk to your child about online safety and the risks of different platforms and websites. Consider talking to your child about these online safety tips.

◆ Protect your passwords.

◆ Don't click on unknown links or popups.

◆ Don't communicate with strangers online.

◆ Never give your personal information online.

◆ Ask an adult before visiting a new website.

Week 1

This week, you can GET READY by:

- ◆ using relative pronouns

- ◆ summarizing a story

- ◆ writing a story

- ◆ designing a T-shirt

- ◆ ordering numbers

- ◆ calculating area

- ◆ using estimation to solve problems

- ◆ using clues to learn about explorers

- ◆ multiplying with number cubes

It's All Relative!

Directions: Complete each sentence with the correct relative pronoun.

A *pronoun* is a word that replaces a noun, such as *he*, *me*, or *we*.

A *relative pronoun* introduces a relative clause, which gives more information about a noun. There are five relative pronouns: *that*, *which*, *who*, *whom*, and *whose*.

1. The letter _____ you gave me was very thoughtful and kind.

2. Babe Ruth, _____ is still considered one of the greatest athletes in all of American sports, will never be forgotten.

3. A fifth grader, _____ main job is to work hard in school, is still learning how to be responsible.

4. Ramona ordered the chocolate cake, _____ is why her sister made the same choice.

USA 33

BABE RUTH

5. The library was full of students, almost all of _____ were looking for research books for their reports that are due on Friday.

6. My favorite pizza topping is pepperoni, _____ was the most popular response in the class survey.

A Visit with Penguins

Directions: Read the passage. Then, answer the questions.

One of the penguins was ready to play. He waddled up the icy hill as fast as he could. Then, he flopped onto his stomach and slid down. Some of the penguins were eating lunch. They swallowed the fish as quickly as the zookeeper could empty the big buckets of food. A few of the penguins were sleeping quietly.

The children watched the penguins for a long time. When it was time to leave the exhibit, all the children were sad to go. Many of the children liked the penguin exhibit best.

1 Write one to two sentences to summarize the passage.

_____

_____

_____

_____

2 What do you think will happen next? Why?

_____

_____

_____

_____

Circus Balloon

Directions: Finish the story below. Include descriptive words in your story. Use the five senses (sight, sound, touch, taste, and smell) to add details.

A man from the circus filled the boy's large, red balloon with helium and tied it to a long ribbon. The boy held the ribbon tightly in his hand and walked over to see the enormous gray elephant. All of a sudden, a brisk wind . . .

_____

_____

_____

_____

_____

_____

_____

_____

_____

_____

_____

_____

_____

_____

_____

T-Shirt Designer

Directions: You are a famous T-shirt designer who designs for different charities. Use the template below to create your newest design!

© **TCM** | Teacher Created Materials

130259—Kids Learn! Getting Ready for 5th Grade

17

Raffle Tickets

Directions: Place the raffle tickets in ascending order, and write the numbers below. Write each of the ticket numbers in word form next to the number. The first one is done for you.

Number	Word Form
1 6,942	six thousand, nine hundred forty-two
2	
3	
4	
5	
6	

Directions: Add 159 to each number below. Write the new number in digits and then in words. The first one has been done for you.

Number	+ 159	New Number
7 6,035	+ 159	*6,194; six thousand, one hundred ninety-four*
8 16,432	+ 159	
9 84,735	+ 159	

Calculating Area

Directions: Calculate the area of each rectangle.

To calculate the area of a rectangle, multiply the length by the width.

Tip

❯ Area = length × width

❯ $A = l \cdot w$

18 ft.

7 ft.

$A = 18 \cdot 7$
$A = 126$ square feet (126 ft.²)

1   5 ft.

3 ft.

$A =$ _____

2   54 cm

43 cm

$A =$ _____

3   50 m

25 m

$A =$ _____

4   12 ft.

9 ft.

$A =$ _____

Solving by Estimating

Directions: Estimate to solve the problems.

Example

Jocelyn played 3 games on a social networking site. She received 321, 489, and 273 points.

About how many points did Jocelyn earn all together?

300 + 500 + 300 = 1,100 points

❶ The same number of cats were curled up on each of 5 chairs. A total of 52 cats were curled up on these chairs. About how many cats were on each chair?

❷ John caught 2,735 pounds of fish. He put them into boxes of 92 pounds each. About how many boxes did he need?

❸ Ann played Math Martians on her computer. She scored 832 in the first game, 505 in the second game, and 397 in her last game. About how many points did she score all together?

Which Explorer Went Where?

Directions: Use the clues to find out why each explorer is famous. Use the chart to eliminate each one based on what you find out in the clues.

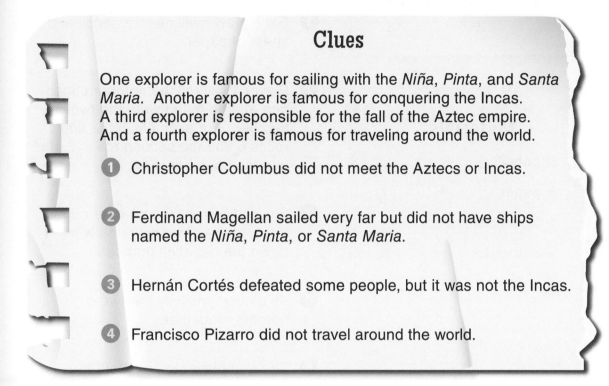

Clues

One explorer is famous for sailing with the *Niña*, *Pinta*, and *Santa Maria*. Another explorer is famous for conquering the Incas. A third explorer is responsible for the fall of the Aztec empire. And a fourth explorer is famous for traveling around the world.

1. Christopher Columbus did not meet the Aztecs or Incas.

2. Ferdinand Magellan sailed very far but did not have ships named the *Niña*, *Pinta*, or *Santa Maria*.

3. Hernán Cortés defeated some people, but it was not the Incas.

4. Francisco Pizarro did not travel around the world.

	Sailed *Niña*, *Pinta*, and *Santa Maria*	Conquered the Incas	Caused the fall of the Aztec Empire	The first to travel around the world
Francisco Pizarro				
Ferdinand Magellan				
Christopher Columbus				
Hernán Cortés				

Roll-the-Numbers Multiplication Game

Number of Players
2–6

Materials
◆ pencils

◆ paper

◆ 2 number cubes

◆ calculator

Directions

1 Each player will need a pencil and a sheet of paper.

2 Player 1 will roll the number cubes one at a time and write the two-digit number. For example, if the first roll is 6 and the second roll is 2, the two-digit number is 62.

3 Player 1 will roll the number cubes again in the same way and write down the two-digit number.

4 All players multiply the two-digit numbers together.

5 The first player to complete the math problem correctly wins the round. Use the calculator to check the answers.

6 Continue playing multiple rounds. Use tally marks to keep score on a sheet of paper. The first player to score 10 tally marks wins the game.

Week 2

This week, you can GET READY by:

◆ capitalizing and punctuating

◆ analyzing a recipe

◆ writing a newspaper article

◆ creating a flyer to advertise a movie

◆ writing numbers in different forms

◆ analyzing data on a line plot

◆ solving multistep word problems

◆ completing a puzzle with expressions

◆ discussing hypothetical questions

Sentence Emergencies

Directions: These sentences need your help! Be a sentence doctor, and fix these sentences. Rewrite the sentences using correct capitalization and punctuation.

1 the students in mr garcias class were reading charlottes web

_____

_____

2 what a wonderful day it is

_____

_____

3 jordan come play with us in griffith park

_____

_____

4 watch out michelle

_____

_____

Reading a Shake Recipe

Directions: Read the recipe. Then, answer the questions.

Ingredients		Equipment
1 cup orange juice, chilled $\frac{1}{2}$ cup milk $\frac{1}{4}$ teaspoon vanilla	1 16-ounce can pitted apricot halves, chilled 1 banana ground nutmeg	measuring cups measuring spoons can opener blender drinking glasses

1 Measure the orange juice, milk, and vanilla into the blender. Add the apricots and their juice. Peel the banana. Break the banana into four pieces; add to the blender.

2 With help from an adult, put the lid on the blender and blend the mixture until it is smooth. Pour the mixture into glasses. Sprinkle the tops with a little nutmeg.

3 Serve cold and enjoy. Makes 4 servings.

To make your table look special, add a vase of flowers and tie pretty bows around some colorful paper napkins. Use rusts, greens, and browns in the fall. A winter table looks nice with reds and greens and pinecones with ivy or greens from trees. Soft colors and small bunny decorations work well in the spring. Red, white, and blue decorations make a perfect table for the 4th of July.

1 The "Shake Recipe" could also be called . . .

A "How to Make Your Table Look Special."

B "How to Use a Blender."

C "A Tasty Treat for All Seasons."

D "How to Throw a Summer Party."

2 The last paragraph was written mainly . . .

A to show that the 4th of July is the best time to have a party.

B to show that apricot-banana shakes should only be served on a table.

C to show how to tie bows around paper napkins.

D to give ideas about how to decorate for the holidays.

Read All About It!

Directions: Write a newspaper article about an event in your neighborhood. Look at a newspaper to find examples of writing for three different purposes: to inform, to entertain, and to persuade. Then, choose a topic and write one type of newspaper article. Make sure to tell about the *who*, *what*, *when*, *where*, *why*, and *how* of the event.

_____

_____

_____

_____

_____

_____

_____

_____

_____

_____

_____

_____

_____

_____

Hollywood Star

Directions: You are a famous actor who will be starring in an upcoming movie. Create a flyer that tells the world about this movie starring you!

Express This Number

Directions: Complete the chart.

Standard Form	Word Form	Expanded Form
1 34,262		
2 781,415		
3	fifty-one thousand, five hundred twenty-seven	
4	nine hundred twenty-three thousand, three hundred thirty-four	
5		20,000 + 3,000 + 400 + 60 + 9

Line Them Up: Making Line Plots

Directions: Use the data about lengths of erasers to make a line plot. Then, answer the questions.

A *line plot* shows data on a number line with various symbols to show frequency, such as an *x*. An *x* is marked each time the same measurement appears. A line plot makes it easy to see which measurements appear most or least often.

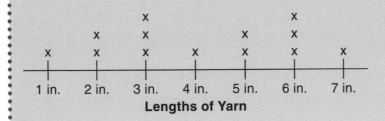

Lengths of Yarn

Lengths of Erasers

$3\frac{1}{2}$ inches ||	$3\frac{1}{4}$ inches |
$2\frac{3}{4}$ inches ||	$2\frac{1}{2}$ inches |||
$1\frac{3}{4}$ inches |||	$1\frac{1}{4}$ inches ||
1 inch |	2 inches ||

❶ Plot the data on this line plot. Make sure to give the line plot a title and label the axis.

Title: _____

❷ What are the most common lengths of erasers? _____

❸ What is the longest eraser? _____

❹ What is the shortest eraser? _____

❺ What is the difference between the longest and shortest erasers? _____

Multistep Word Problems

Directions: Solve the problems. Show the steps you take to find the answer.

1 Sergio enjoys collecting stamps as a hobby. He collected 12 stamps in June, 24 in July, and 29 in August. Then he decided to give 18 to his brother. How many stamps does Sergio have left?

2 Lily ate 3 strawberries at breakfast and had 2 times that many for lunch. If she wants to eat 20 strawberries in one day, how many will she need to have for dessert?

3 Parker made 75 cents at his lemonade stand on Saturday. He made 2 times as much as that on Sunday. Parker wants to buy 2 candy bars that cost $1.00 each. Does he have enough money? If so, how much change will he get?

Many Ways to Say 10

Directions: Fill in the grid with the missing expressions.

Every mini-grid, every column, and every row must have each of these number sentences:

8 + 2	20 ÷ 2	20 × 0.5
10 × 1	15 − 5	100 ÷ 10

	8 + 2	10 × 1			15 − 5
	20 × 0.5		8 + 2	10 × 1	
100 ÷ 10	15 − 5	20 × 0.5		8 + 2	
8 + 2	10 × 1		100 ÷ 10	15 − 5	
		15 − 5	10 × 1		8 + 2
10 × 1	20 ÷ 2				

Family Discussions

Number of Players
2–6

Materials
◆ *Discussion Cards* (page 103)

Directions

1 Cut apart the *Discussion Cards* on page 103, and place them facedown in a pile.

2 Each player takes a turn drawing a card and answers the question first.

3 In clockwise order, the other players take turns answering the question without repeating or copying what has already been said. Each player must support his or her answer with reasons why.

4 Once all players have commented on the card, discuss the similarities and differences between the responses.

5 Continue until all cards have been discussed.

If you could be any superhero, who would you be and why?

If you could be really good at something, what would it be and why?

If you could meet anyone, past or present, who would it be and what would you ask that person?

If you could be any animal, what would it be and why?

What do you believe is the most important job? Why?

If you could invent anything, what would it be and how would it help people?

Week 3

This week, you can GET READY by:

◆ fixing run-on sentences

◆ analyzing opinions

◆ writing a narrative

◆ designing a dog park

◆ comparing numbers

◆ making equivalent fractions

◆ solving fraction word problems

◆ using clues to figure out a seating chart

◆ building a paper tower

Stop That Sentence!

Directions: Correct each run-on sentence by rewriting it into two sentences.

 A sentence that combines two complete thoughts as one is called a *run-on sentence*.

1 My books are on the table my math book is on top.

_____

_____

2 They were closing the store it was time to go home.

_____

_____

3 Watch out for the slippery ice you could fall and hurt yourself.

_____

_____

4 I got a new blue shirt my blue shoes match perfectly.

_____

_____

5 My brother made the team will I be able to play baseball someday?

_____

_____

It's a Matter of Opinion

Directions: Read the opinion paragraph. Put a box around the opinion and underline the supporting details. Then, respond to the question.

Everybody needs to have a pet. Have you ever noticed that people who do not have pets are grouchier than those who do? If they were greeted whenever they came home by a furry creature thrilled to see them, they would be a lot less grouchy. A pet is affectionate and a good companion. Pets like to snuggle and be with people. Also, pets are always positive. If you give them a special treat, they act as if you've given them the world's largest diamond or the fastest car. They shake with joy, leap, and prance. If you've had a hard day, they still greet you with enthusiasm. They don't care what you do. You can be a complete failure, and they still treat you as if you were a king or queen. Pets love you unconditionally. If you forget to feed them, they forgive you the moment you remember. Pets are also good safety devices. They can scare away strangers. They can warn you if there is a fire or something wrong inside or outside the house. All they ask in return is a bowl of food, some water, and some TLC (tender, loving care). If everybody had a pet, everybody would go around smiling.

How does the author use reasons and evidence to support the opinion?

_____

_____

_____

_____

_____

_____

You're a Star!

Directions: Imagine that one day you become very famous. Write a story about the success that brings you fame. In the story, explain how and why you became famous. Also, tell about what other important things you might do in the future.

YOUR NAME

The Most Outrageous Dog Park

Directions: You have been hand selected to create the most outrageous dog park. Draw an aerial view (view from above) of the park, and include a legend that explains each area.

Legend

© **TCM** |Teacher Created Materials

130259—Kids Learn! Getting Ready for 5th Grade   **37**

Let's Compare!

Directions: Compare the numbers. Use the symbols >, <, or =.

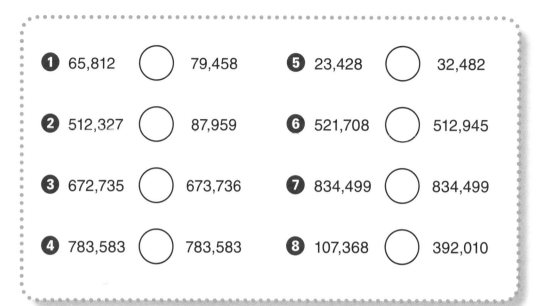

1 65,812 ◯ 79,458   **5** 23,428 ◯ 32,482

2 512,327 ◯ 87,959   **6** 521,708 ◯ 512,945

3 672,735 ◯ 673,736   **7** 834,499 ◯ 834,499

4 783,583 ◯ 783,583   **8** 107,368 ◯ 392,010

✏️ **Choose a question, 1–8. Explain how you solved it.**

_____

_____

_____

_____

_____

Making Equivalent Fractions

To make equivalent fractions, multiply the numerator and denominator by the same number.

$$\frac{1}{5} \times \frac{2}{2} = \frac{2}{10} \qquad\qquad \frac{1}{5} \times \frac{3}{3} = \frac{3}{15}$$

Multiplying the numerator and denominator by the same number is the same as multiplying by 1.

Directions: Look at each fraction below. Write two more fractions that are equivalent in value.

1 $\frac{2}{3}$ = _____ = _____

2 $\frac{3}{8}$ = _____ = _____

3 $\frac{4}{5}$ = _____ = _____

4 $\frac{9}{10}$ = _____ = _____

5 $\frac{8}{13}$ = _____ = _____

Fraction Word Problems

Directions: Read the word problems. Show your work in the boxes.

1 Nola invited 15 friends to her birthday party. The girls ate pizza for dinner. They ate $\frac{2}{4}$ of the pepperoni pizza and $\frac{1}{4}$ of the cheese pizza. How much pizza did they eat altogether?

2 On Monday, Sergio made $\frac{3}{10}$ of his shots in the basketball game. On Tuesday, he made $\frac{1}{10}$ of his shots in the basketball game. What fractions of his shots did he make?

3 The cook needed to hard-boil some eggs. She used $\frac{1}{2}$ dozen eggs for breakfast and $\frac{3}{4}$ dozen eggs for lunch. How many eggs did she use altogether?

Dinner Table Seating Chart

Directions: Use the clues below to discover the seating chart for dinner.

Clues

George Washington, Benjamin Franklin, Thomas Jefferson, Alexander Hamilton, James Madison, and John Adams met for dinner. Benjamin Franklin chose the seat in the middle and next to the first president of the United States. The second president of the United States sat next to the third president of the United States. Thomas Jefferson sat across from George Washington. James Madison sat next to a person who never served as president. Alexander Hamilton sat across from the person who served as president during the War of 1812.

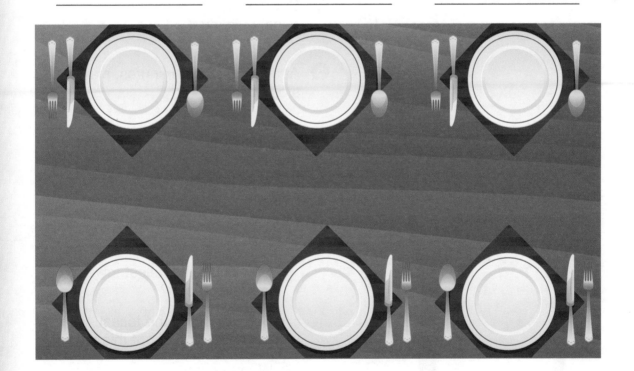

The Tallest Paper Tower

Number of Players
2–6

Materials

◆ paper

◆ tape

◆ timer

◆ measuring tape

◆ scissors (*optional*)

Directions

1 Distribute the same number of papers and one foot of tape to each player.

2 Each player will use the paper and tape to build the tallest tower in five minutes. Allow scissors to encourage cutting paper. **Note:** The tower must be able to stand on its own.

3 Allow two minutes for players to plan their towers.

4 Set the timer for five minutes and begin building the towers.

5 At the end of five minutes, players stop building.

6 Use the measuring tape to measure the paper towers. The person with the tallest paper tower wins!

7 Discuss the following questions:

◆ How could the tallest tower be improved upon?

◆ Besides being the tallest, what is the best thing about this tower?

◆ What are some other ways a person could build a taller tower?

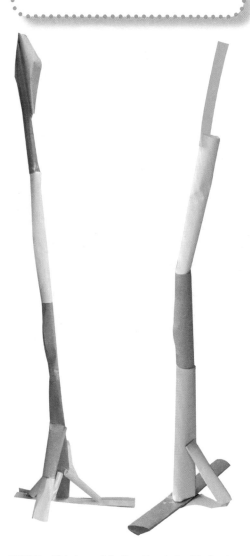

Week 4

This week, you can GET READY by:

- practicing homophones
- analyzing evidence to support claims
- writing a persuasive letter
- designing a room
- rounding decimals
- matching fractions to expressions
- solving fraction word problems
- solving a brain teaser
- racing to solve math problems

To, Too, or Two?

Directions: Write the correct homophone of *to*, *too*, or *two* on the lines.

1. I'm going _____ be in a dance recital tomorrow. I'll be wearing my new tutu, which is a little _____ big. _____ of my friends will dance, _____. I'm _____ excited _____ sleep, but I have _____ go _____ bed.

2. The leaves were falling from the trees as I walked _____ school. It must be fall, which I call autumn, _____. I know that there are _____ more weeks until Halloween. I can't wait _____ go trick-or-treating! My friend Alexa is going _____ walk with me, _____. We will remember _____ say "Thank you!" after we get our candy. I hope that I get at least _____ lollipops _____ eat!

An Author's Use of Evidence

Directions: Read the text. Put a box around the author's claims or main points. Then, underline all evidence that is included to support each claim. Finally, answer the questions on a separate sheet of paper.

Dear Restaurant Manager,

Though I have enjoyed your food in the past, I believe that the quality of your business has suffered recently and that certain issues demand your prompt attention. Recently, I was in your pizzeria and was extremely disappointed in the service that I received. I arrived with my family and was told it would be a 30-minute wait. Over an hour passed before we were seated, and no one apologized for this inconvenience.

Though our server took our order promptly, we waited over 20 minutes for drinks and appetizers to arrive. When the food arrived, the order was wrong! The server was quite rude when we asked for the items that we ordered.

We were very surprised to see that your customer service has suffered so horribly. There was no mention of taking things off our bill, no visit from you, not even a thank you. I like to support local businesses, but I can't spend money on restaurant experiences such as this one.

Please check into this matter immediately and do what you can to change your customers' experiences. We want to be loyal customers, but we need to see some sign of improvement first before we will visit your pizzeria for a future meal.

Sincerely,
Fred Gandley

1 Were all claims supported by credible evidence? Explain.

2 Do you think the restaurant manager will change his actions? Explain.

Letter to the Mayor

Directions: Write a letter to your mayor asking him or her to consider a new facility in your town, such as a skate park or an arcade. In the letter, be sure to support your request with reasons why the facility should be built.

_____

_____

_____

_____

_____

_____

_____

_____

_____

_____

_____

_____

_____

_____

_____

_____

Room Designer Extraordinaire!

Directions: You are an experienced designer and have been hired to create the most amazing room. In the sections below, either draw or cut out pictures from magazines to show what this space will look like.

Fabric

Paint Colors

Furniture

Something Unusual

Rounding Decimals

Directions: Round each decimal to the nearest whole number.

1 50.8

2 96.24

3 21.075

_____

_____

_____

Directions: Round each decimal to the nearest tenths place.

4 5.89

5 13.73

6 45.32

_____

_____

_____

Directions: Round each decimal to the nearest hundredths place.

7 3.908

8 851.431

9 0.634

_____

_____

_____

10 Why must you round to the nearest hundredth when dealing with money? Explain your thinking using complete sentences.

_____

_____

_____

Match the Fraction

Directions: Match the fractions to the correct expressions.

1 $\frac{5}{6}$

2 $\frac{9}{6}$

3 $\frac{18}{10}$

4 $\frac{4}{10}$

5 $\frac{9}{5}$

6 $\frac{12}{8}$

A $4 \times \frac{1}{10}$

B $2 \times \frac{6}{8}$

C $5 \times \frac{1}{6}$

D $3 \times \frac{3}{6}$

E $9 \times \frac{1}{5}$

F $6 \times \frac{3}{10}$

Real World Fractions

Directions: Read the word problems. Solve the problems by multiplying the whole numbers by fractions. Show your work.

1 Chloe has 12 pencils. If $\frac{3}{4}$ of them are broken, how many pencils are broken?

Work It Out	Answer

2 Mr. Garcia baked 24 cupcakes. He will bring $\frac{1}{3}$ of them to a party. How many cupcakes will he bring to the party?

Work It Out	Answer

3 The soccer players kicked 18 soccer balls to the goal. If $\frac{2}{3}$ of the balls made it in the goal, how many soccer balls did not make it in the goal?

Work It Out	Answer

Connect the Dots

Directions: Connect all the dots by drawing only three continuous straight lines.

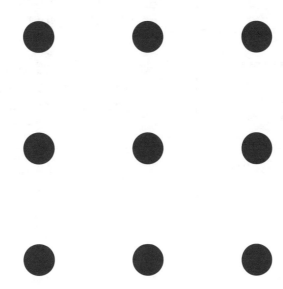

Reflection Questions

1 What was the first strategy you used to figure out this puzzle?

_____

_____

2 How many trials and errors did it take?

_____

_____

3 On a separate sheet of paper, create your own puzzle for someone to solve.

Who Can Solve It?

Number of Players
2–6

Materials

- *Math Problems Flashcards* (page 105)
- pencils
- paper

Directions

1. Each player will need a pencil and a sheet of paper.

2. Cut apart the *Math Problems Flashcards* on page 105, and place them facedown in a pile.

3. Each player takes a turn drawing a card from the pile and turning it over so that everyone can see it. The goal is to solve the problem on the flashcard as fast as possible.

4. The first person to complete the math problem correctly wins!

5. Repeat until all the cards have been solved.

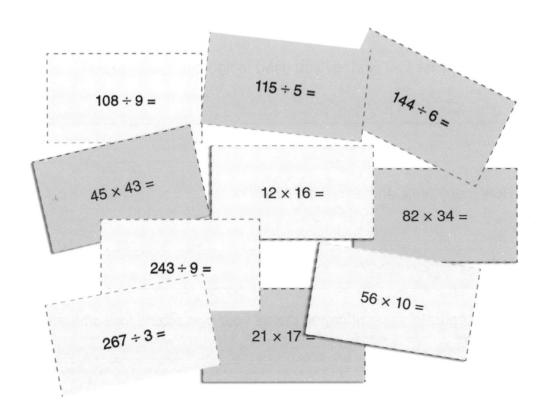

108 ÷ 9 =

115 ÷ 5 =

144 ÷ 6 =

45 × 43 =

12 × 16 =

82 × 34 =

243 ÷ 9 =

56 × 10 =

267 ÷ 3 =

21 × 17 =

Week 5

This week, you can GET READY by:

- using adjectives and adverbs in sentences
- making inferences
- researching and writing about domains of life
- creating an identity
- multiplying two-digit numbers
- turning fractions into decimals
- drawing and naming shapes
- identifying analogies
- making squares with toothpicks

Adjectives and Adverbs

Directions: Add adjectives and adverbs to the sentences to make them more specific and interesting. Then, reread your sentences to make sure the adjectives are ordered correctly in each sentence.

Adjectives are used to modify nouns and pronouns. *Adverbs* are used to modify verbs, adjectives, and other adverbs. Both are used to make writing more specific and interesting.

Example without adjectives and adverbs: The convertible ran into the truck.

Example with adjectives and adverbs: The **red, shiny Mustang** convertible **suddenly** ran into the **four-door, white Dodge pickup** truck.

1 The dog barked at the cat.

_____

_____

2 I hit the ball.

_____

_____

3 Mei Ling ate lunch.

_____

_____

4 Everyone watched Rafael play basketball.

_____

_____

Inferring from a Picture

Directions: Look at the picture. Think about what might be happening. Then, answer the questions.

Making an *inference* means to draw a conclusion based on given information. Some authors do not explain everything fully. They expect readers to "read between the lines."

1 What are the animals doing? How do you know?

_____

_____

_____

2 Why are the animals facing each other?

_____

_____

_____

It's Alive!

Directions: Research one of the three major domains of life (bacteria, archaea, and eukaryota). Use the Internet and/or nonfiction books to learn more about a domain. Write two paragraphs with facts and details about the domain.

© **TCM** | Teacher Created Materials

True Identity

Directions: Below is a picture of a face. Who is this person—a villain, a princess, or someone else? Add to this face to reveal this person's identity.

Multiply Using a Standard Algorithm

Example: Multiply 67 × 43

Step 1: Multiply by the ones column.	**Step 2:** Multiply by the tens column. **Remember:** The 4 in the tens place represents 40.	**Step 3:** Add the partial products.
67 × **43** 201 ← 3 × 67	67 × **43** 201 2,680 ← 40 × 67	67 × 43 201 ← partial product + 2,680 ← partial product 2,881

Directions: Find the product using the standard algorithm.

1. 46
   × 32

2. 51
   × 69

3. 25
   × 84

4. 94
   × 16

5. Half of Mrs. Sullivan's 32 students brought in 12 notebooks each and the other half brought in 18 folders each. How many notebooks and folders do they have to share among all of the students?

_____

Turning a Fraction into a Decimal

A **decimal** is a fraction whose denominator is a power of ten (10, 100, 1,000, and so on). The numerator in the fraction is written in the decimal place values to the right of the decimal point. A decimal, like a fraction, is not a whole number. It is part of a number.

$$\frac{4}{10} = 0.4 \text{ four tenths}$$

$$\frac{4}{100} = 0.04 \text{ four hundredths}$$

$$\frac{4}{1000} = 0.004 \text{ four thousandths}$$

Directions: Change the fractions into decimals.

1. $\frac{5}{10}$ _____

2. $\frac{9}{10}$ _____

3. $\frac{2}{10}$ _____

4. $\frac{7}{100}$ _____

5. $\frac{4}{100}$ _____

6. $\frac{26}{100}$ _____

7. $\frac{80}{1000}$ _____

8. $\frac{4}{10}$ _____

9. $\frac{6}{100}$ _____

10. $\frac{98}{100}$ _____

Features of Shapes

Directions: Draw and name each shape based on the description.

Description	Shape
1 • 3 sides • 1 right angle	
2 • parallel and perpendicular line segments • 4 right angles	
3 • 4 sides • acute and obtuse angles • 1 pair of parallel line segments	
4 • 4 sides • no right angles • 2 pairs of parallel line segments	
5 • 3 sides • only acute angles	
6 • parallel and perpendicular line segments • 4 right angles • all sides equal	

60 130259—Kids Learn! Getting Ready for 5th Grade

© **TCM** | Teacher Created Materials

Awesome Analogies

Directions: Write a word to complete each analogy.

> **Example**
>
> teacher : student :: parent : child

1 pig : oink :: dog : _____

2 duck : quack :: cow : _____

3 fish : swim :: cheetah : _____

4 today : tomorrow :: yesterday : _____

5 gray : black :: pink : _____

Directions: Create your own analogies. Remember to include the colons.

6 _____

7 _____

Toothpicks and Squares

Number of Players

2–6

Materials

◆ *Direction Cards* (page 107)

◆ toothpicks

Directions

1. Each player begins by making this shape using 12 toothpicks.

2. Cut apart and shuffle the *Direction Cards* (page 107). Place the cards facedown in a pile.

3. Turn over a card to reveal the command.

4. The player who finishes the command first wins.

5. Set the toothpicks back to the shape above.

6. Then, repeat using a new card with a new command.

Week 6

This week, you can GET READY by:

- ◆ sequencing sentences
- ◆ determining text structure
- ◆ writing a review of a movie or a television show
- ◆ creating art around a hole
- ◆ solving problems with remainders
- ◆ turning fractions into decimals
- ◆ multiplying whole numbers by fractions
- ◆ using clues to solve problems
- ◆ moving items in creative ways

Put Them in Order

Directions: Read the sentences. Write numbers on the lines to place them in order. Then, write a paragraph to continue the story.

_____ I got out of bed and looked in the mirror.

_____ I ran to my mother to show her what had happened.

_____ She said, "It appears that those seeds you swallowed yesterday have been planted inside you."

_____ I woke up one morning feeling strange.

_____ Then, she looked in the phone book for a good gardener to come over to trim me.

_____ What a shock I got when I saw a plant growing out of my ears!

_____ I am feeling better now, but I still have to water myself every day.

_____

_____

_____

_____

_____

_____

_____

_____

Identifying Text Structure

Directions: A text's *structure* is determined by the author's purpose for writing and the way he or she organizes the ideas. Use the chart to help you identify the text structure of the text below.

Text Structure	Definition	Signal Words
chronology	describes events or steps in order	before, first, next, soon, later, finally
comparison	shows how two or more ideas are alike and different	same as, similar, both, instead of, on the other hand
cause and effect	describes events and what made them happen	so, because, therefore, if, then, as a result, consequently, for this reason
problem and solution	describes a problem and possible solutions	question is, dilemma is, to solve this, one answer is, one option is

How to Make a Cabbage-Water Acid/Base Detector

First, take a head of red cabbage and cut it into strips approximately 1 cm (0.25 in.) by 4 cm (1.37 in.). Next, measure 50 grams (1.76 ounces) of the chopped cabbage into a glass beaker. Cover with 4 times the weight of the cabbage, which in this case will be 200 grams (7 ounces) of water. Heat the beakers to 100 degrees Celsius (212 degrees Fahrenheit) until the liquid begins to boil. Continue to cook the mixture for five more minutes. After five minutes, turn off the heat and allow the mixture to cool. Once it reaches room temperature, strain out the cabbage pieces and discard. The water should be bluish purple. It can now be used to determine whether substances are acids or bases. Acids will turn the water pink, while bases will react to turn the water teal.

Text structure: _____

Evidence: _____

_____

_____

Movie Review

Directions: Write a review of a movie or TV program. Include details about the plot and descriptions of the characters. Give specific details to support your main idea, and include how various techniques used by the actors and producers contributed to the message or main idea of the movie.

There's a Hole in My Paper!

Directions: What can you draw that has a hole in it? Draw a picture that incorporates this hole in a creative way.

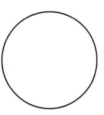

What's Remaining?

Some division problems divide evenly, and other times, you are left with remainders.

$$27 \div 9 = 3$$

But what happens when you divide 29 by 9?
9 divides into 29 3 times, but there are 2 left over.
This solution has a remainder of 2. It can be written 3 R2.

Directions: Solve the problems. The answers may or may not have remainders.

1 $8\overline{)9}$

2 $9\overline{)39}$

3 $6\overline{)96}$

4 $4\overline{)87}$

5 $7\overline{)102}$

6 $3\overline{)22}$

7 $6\overline{)648}$

8 $8\overline{)113}$

9 $5\overline{)125}$

Getting Decimals in Line

Directions: Change each group of fractions into decimals. Then, place the decimals in order from greatest to least.

1 $\dfrac{5}{10}$ $\dfrac{9}{10}$ $\dfrac{6}{100}$ $\dfrac{7}{100}$

_____   _____   _____   _____

2 $\dfrac{9}{10}$ $\dfrac{6}{100}$ $\dfrac{4}{100}$ $\dfrac{61}{1000}$

_____   _____   _____   _____

3 $\dfrac{4}{10}$ $\dfrac{12}{100}$ $\dfrac{8}{10}$ $\dfrac{2}{1000}$

_____   _____   _____   _____

4 $\dfrac{9}{10}$ $\dfrac{6}{1000}$ $\dfrac{9}{100}$ $\dfrac{57}{100}$

_____   _____   _____   _____

Directions: Mark the letter of each value in the correct location on the number line.

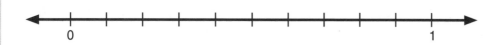

0   1

5 **A**   0.75

6 **B**   0.29

7 **C**   0.15

8 **D**   0.50

Fraction Party Riddles

Directions: Read the word problems. Solve the problems by multiplying the whole numbers by fractions. Show your work.

1 The Niles family is having a barbecue. They are inviting family and friends. If they want to grill $\frac{2}{3}$ pound of ribs for each person and 15 people are eating ribs, how many ribs do they need to grill?

2 Some people at the Niles family party will be eating salmon. If the Niles family wants to cook $\frac{3}{5}$ pound of salmon for each person and 12 people are eating salmon, how much salmon do they need to cook?

3 The Niles family wants everyone to eat dessert, too. If they estimate that each guest will have about $\frac{1}{6}$ of a pie, how many pies do they need to serve 24 guests?

What Happened?

Directions: Read the scenarios. Then, describe what happened.

Jack is inside a boot. Puddles of water and glass surround the boot on the floor. He won't survive unless he is submerged in water soon. In the space below, explain what you think happened.

_____

_____

_____

_____

_____

_____

You drive a limousine. There are six people inside, including three adults and three children. Two of them are female and the rest are male. Most of the passengers have either blue or green eyes, but one has brown eyes. What color are the driver's eyes?

_____

_____

_____

_____

_____

_____

Move Those Things!

Number of Players
2–6

Materials

◆ 3 marshmallows

◆ 1 egg

◆ 1 balloon (blown up)

◆ 1 tennis ball

◆ 1 tablespoon

◆ 3 toothpicks

◆ 3 pencils

◆ 6 paper clips

◆ timer

Directions

1. Place all the items on the counter.

2. Work as a team to move the items from the counter to a table at least four feet (1.2 meters) away.

3. Your teammates cannot touch the items with their hands. Instead, move the items using these utensils: tablespoon, toothpicks, pencils, and paper clips. These utensils can only be used one time.

4. Set the timer for five minutes, and see if your team can do this task!

5. When the time is up, talk about the activity using these questions:

    ◆ How else could the items have been moved without dropping them?

    ◆ What would you change if given another chance to move these items?

    ◆ What else would you add to these utensils to help you move the items more easily?

Week 7

This week, you can GET READY by:

- using clues to figure out vocabulary
- learning about the Battle of Shiloh
- writing about a funny moment
- describing steps to draw a picture
- using long division to uncover a message
- calculating areas
- figuring out times
- learning about important Americans
- experimenting with dough and weight

Clue Me In!

Directions: Read about these natural elements. Use clues from the text to determine the meaning of each underlined word.

Aluminum

Aluminum is a natural element. Even though it is natural, it is never found on its own in nature. It has to be <u>extracted</u> from other minerals. It is used to make foil, cans, pots and pans, and even airplanes.

Clue: _____

Definition: _____

_____

_____

Iron

There is an <u>abundance</u> of iron in the universe. It is found inside Earth, in the soil, in water, and even in stars! Just about everywhere you look, this natural element can be found.

Clue: _____

Definition: _____

_____

_____

A Letter of Despair

Directions: Read the letter. Underline parts that include lots of description. Write notes in the margins about how the author has made you feel while reading the letter.

My Dearest Brother Frederick,

I have never imagined such horror as I have seen these last few days at Shiloh. There were so many men who left the mortal realm. There were so many women made widows. I am not sure I can bear to think upon it, but I know that if I do not write these things down, they will haunt me forever.

The first day of fighting was a clear Southern victory. General Johnston had learned Union reinforcements were on the way. He wanted to attack before they arrived. His plan was sound, but the fighting was fierce. I lived through the bloodiest day of the war thus far. May there never be another like it! General Johnston himself was slain by a cannon blast, and General Beauregard took over command. Our own dear friends, Kurt Flanders and Willem Simpson, fell. My heart grieves for them and for their families back home in Georgia.

General Buell arrived with Grant's reinforcements. Suddenly, the advantage was no longer ours. There were 45,000 men with the North. Our numbers were maybe half of that. In the end, General Beauregard was forced to withdraw our troops back to Corinth. The victory we had celebrated the day before felt like too little gain for too much loss.

Your Loving Brother,
John

That's Funny!

Directions: Write a journal entry about a funny or embarrassing moment in your life.

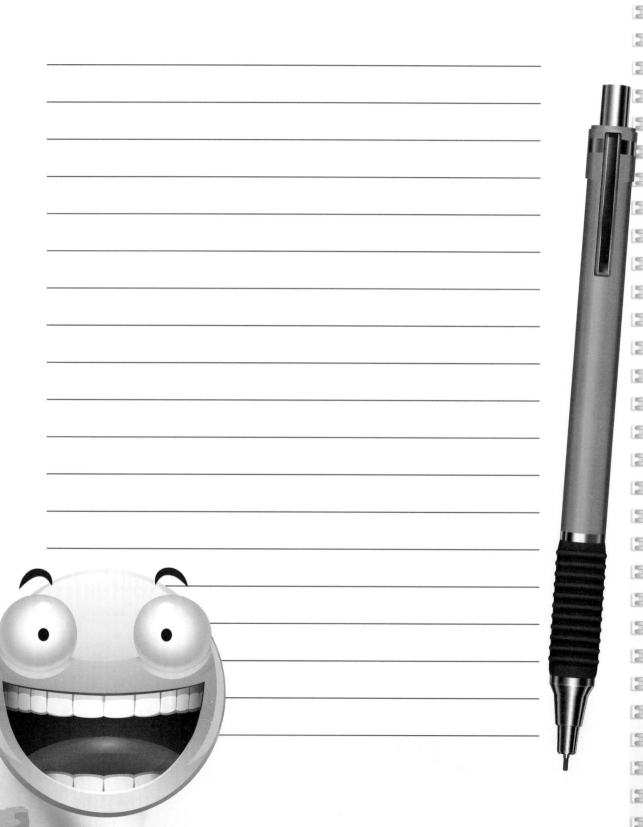

© **TCM** | Teacher Created Materials

What Does It Look Like?

Directions: Draw one thing in the box below. Then, write detailed steps explaining how to draw it on the lines below. Have someone draw the same picture using your steps. Then, compare the pictures!

1 _____

_____

2 _____

_____

3 _____

_____

4 _____

_____

Get the Message!

Directions: Find the quotient using any method. Use scratch paper to help you. Match the solutions below to uncover a famous quotation by Abraham Lincoln.

T 15)‾567‾   A 4)‾600‾   G 6)‾1,425‾

W 12)‾879‾   V 60)‾903‾   U 3)‾852‾

J 36)‾5,490‾   B 5)‾6,214‾   E 25)‾625‾

H 18)‾600‾   D 82)‾7,545‾   N 10)‾3,045‾

O 19)‾361‾   Y 56)‾1,234‾   R 11)‾91‾

73 R3	33 R6	150	37 R12	25	15 R3	25	8 R3

22 R2	19	284

150	8 R3	25

,

1,242 R4	25	

	150

237 R3	19	19	92 R1

19	304 R5	25

.

130259—Kids Learn! Getting Ready for 5th Grade

Accurate Areas

Directions: Measure the edges of these rectangles in centimeters. Round your measurements to the nearest centimeter. Then, calculate the area.

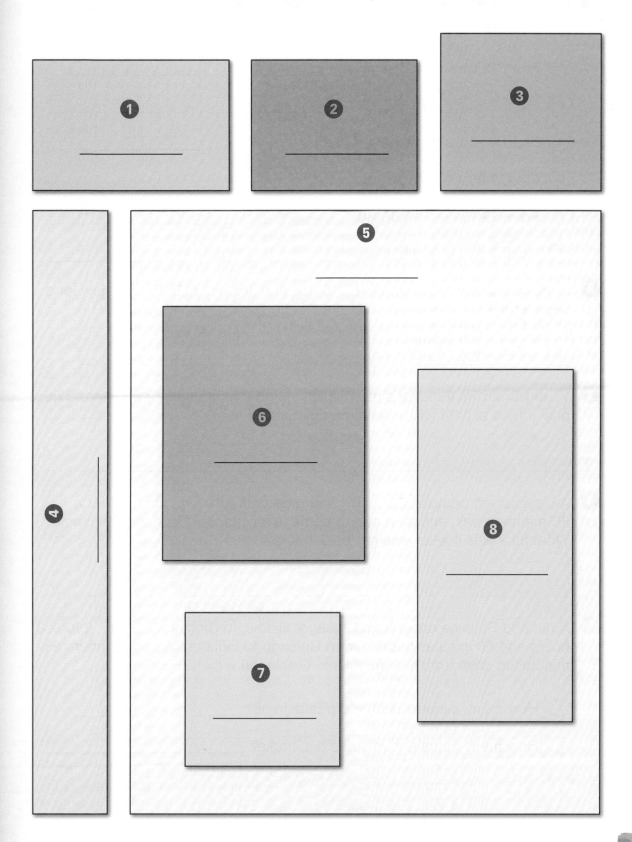

How Long Does It Take?

Directions: Read and solve each problems.

1 Calculate the length of time in hours and minutes between each of the following sets of times:

(A) From 12:00 A.M. to 7:20 A.M. _____

(B) From 7:20 P.M. to 11:10 P.M. _____

(C) From 6:15 A.M. to 10:50 A.M. _____

(D) From 2:05 A.M. to 3:10 A.M. _____

(E) From 12:15 P.M. to 6:00 P.M. _____

(F) From 7:10 A.M. to 11:25 A.M. _____

2 A movie at the theater starts at 7:10 P.M. and finishes at 9:25 P.M. How long does it run?

_____

3 Yi and Brian went to see a play, which lasted 2 hours and 12 minutes. The play ended at 3:04 P.M. What time did it start?

_____

4 A bicyclist left home at 6:30 A.M. She rode until 8:10 A.M., stopped for a 20-minute break, and then cycled home, which took 1 hour and 50 minutes. What time was it when she got back home?

_____

5 Nihal and Shanice drove from Chicago, Illinois, to Cincinnati, Ohio. It took 3 hours and 50 minutes to drive from Chicago to Indianapolis and 2 hours 25 minutes to drive from Indianapolis to Cincinnati.

(A) How many minutes did the trip take in all? _____

(B) How many hours and minutes did it take? _____

Who Is Responsible for What?

Directions: Use the clues to figure out who is responsible for what event in history. Match each person or persons with the correct event.

Clues

Teddy Roosevelt was a rugged man who loved hunting and the outdoors. Lewis and Clark lived for adventure and exploring new territories. Benjamin Franklin was constantly inventing things and making life easier for Americans. James Madison had a knack for writing laws. Martin Luther King Jr.'s famous speech was about his dream that his children would be treated the same as other children, regardless of skin color. A famous suffragist, Susan B. Anthony, gave speeches and had people sign petitions.

1 Who was responsible for helping to get women the right to vote?

_____

2 Who was responsible for going on an expedition west to discover new land?

_____

3 Who was responsible for working for equal rights for African Americans?

_____

4 Who was responsible for writing the United States Constitution?

_____

5 Who organized the first United States mail service?

_____

6 Who designated land to be protected by the United States National Park Service?

_____

Dough Boats

Number of Players

2–6

Materials

◆ clay or molding dough

◆ timer

◆ pennies or paper clips

Directions

1 Give each person the same amount of clay or molding dough.

2 Set the timer for 10 minutes. Players will use their clay or dough to create a boat that can hold the most pennies or paper clips.

3 Fill the sink with water, and place the boats in the sink. One by one, place a penny or a paper clip in each boat.

4 The last boat to stay afloat wins!

5 Discuss these questions after the contest.

◆ What was different about the boat that lasted the longest?

◆ Why do you think this boat stayed afloat with the most weight?

◆ What would you do to improve your boat?

Week 8

This week, you can GET READY by:

- ◆ determining the meanings of idioms
- ◆ answering text-dependent questions
- ◆ writing step-by-step instructions for doing something
- ◆ drawing an amazing machine
- ◆ identifying patterns
- ◆ creating equations to reach a target number
- ◆ determining prices based on pounds
- ◆ thinking about genetics
- ◆ creating sentences from words

Idioms

Directions: Determine the meanings of the idioms.

 Idioms are expressions with meanings different from the literal meanings.

1 When Angelica said, "That movie took my breath away," what did she mean?

_____

_____

2 "When Dad put his foot down, my brother did better in school," said Boris. What did Boris mean?

_____

_____

3 Dana stood and said, "I guess I'll hit the road now." What did Dana mean?

_____

_____

4 When Mario said that he was under the weather, what did he mean?

_____

_____

5 When Nicholas said that he slept like a log last night, what did he mean?

_____

_____

The Crazier the Better

Directions: Read the passage. Then, answer the questions. Use text from the story to support your answers.

> To José, Crazy Hair Day was the best day of the school year. He loved being goofy, and he loved making his classmates laugh. On Crazy Hair Day, he usually managed to do both of those things very well.
>
> In second grade, he colored his hair purple and spiked it into a cone shape like a troll doll. In third grade, he braided his hair into 16 tiny braids. He wrapped a pipe cleaner around each braid and stuck paper airplanes to the ends. He called his design Fly Boy. That was awesome!
>
> This year would be no exception. José had been planning it since September. That's when he had found an abandoned bird's nest on the way to school. He had saved it in a plastic bag all these months. It was going to be the perfect Crazy Hair Day accessory!

1 Why does José like Crazy Hair Day?

_____

_____

_____

2 Describe José's third-grade Crazy Hair Day style.

_____

_____

_____

3 What do you think José plans to do for this year's Crazy Hair Day?

_____

_____

_____

Here's How You Do It!

Directions: Think of something you know how to do well, such as playing a sport or playing an instrument. Then, write step-by-step instructions that explain how to do it.

_____

_____

_____

_____

_____

_____

_____

_____

_____

_____

_____

_____

_____

_____

_____

_____

The Most Amazing Machine

Directions: You have invented the most amazing machine! Draw the machine. Then, add notes to the drawing to explain why it is the most amazing machine ever!

Looking for a Pattern Problems

Directions: Solve each problem and show your work.

Problem A

Complete each number line. Then, write the rule.

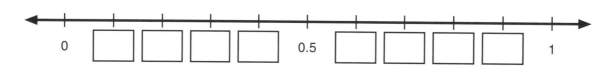

Rule: _____

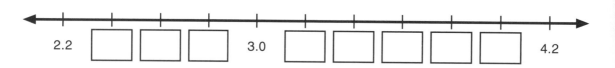

Rule: _____

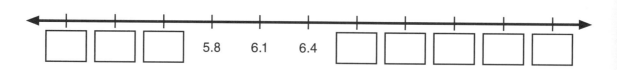

Rule: _____

Problem B

Create your own number line. Then, write the rule.

Rule: _____

Target Number

Directions: Use the given numbers to reach each target number. You may use parentheses, multiplication, division, addition, and/or subtraction. Write your equation on the line provided.

1 Target number: 3

1	2	3	4	3

_____

2 Target number: 2

6	7	8	9	10

_____

3 Target number: 12

3	3	3	5	6

_____

4 Target number: 5

4	5	5	10	10

_____

© **TCM** |Teacher Created Materials

Consumer Math

Directions: The Corner Market advertises their fruit prices by the pound on a chalkboard outside the store every week. Use the prices for this week to answer the questions.

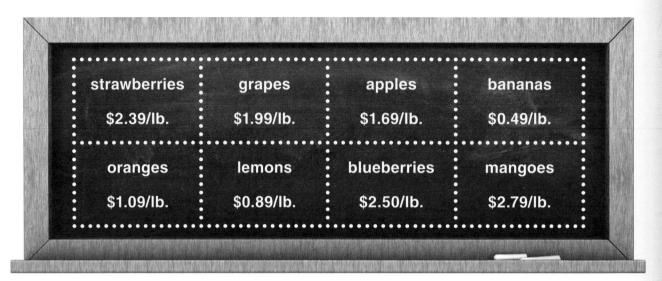

strawberries	grapes	apples	bananas
$2.39/lb.	$1.99/lb.	$1.69/lb.	$0.49/lb.
oranges	lemons	blueberries	mangoes
$1.09/lb.	$0.89/lb.	$2.50/lb.	$2.79/lb.

1 Charlie's grandmother gave him a $20.00 bill. If he buys 3 lbs. of bananas, 2 lbs. of oranges, and 3 lbs. of grapes, how much change will Charlie give back to his grandmother?

_____

2 Kathryn has 10 dollars and needs to buy 5 lbs. of strawberries. Will she be able to buy all 5 lbs.? Show how much over or under Kathryn will be.

_____

3 Hannah buys 1 lb. of each kind of fruit on the chalkboard. How much will this cost her?

_____

4 Mason is going to have a lemonade stand. His aunt buys him 10 lbs. of lemons. If he sells each cup of lemonade for a quarter, how many cups does he need to sell to pay her back?

_____

Eye Color

Directions: A wife and husband have a son with blue eyes. The wife has blue eyes (bb). The husband has brown eyes (Bb). Blue eyes are recessive, and brown eyes are dominant. Study the chart showing the eye colors their children could have. Then, answer the questions.

Key

B = dominant brown

b = recessive blue

Wife

	b	b
B	Bb	Bb
b	bb	bb

Husband

1 How likely is it that they would have a blue-eyed child?

_____

_____

2 Create a chart like this for two different people who each have brown eyes (Bb).

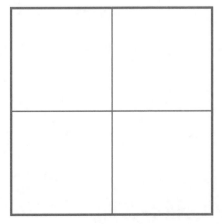

Word Sentences

Number of Players
2–6

Materials
◆ *Word Cards* (page 109)

◆ paper

◆ pencils or pens

Directions

1 Give each player a pencil or pen and a sheet of paper.

2 Cut apart the *Word Cards* on page 109, and place them facedown in a pile.

3 One player will turn over the top card.

4 Players will write four-word sentences using the four letters found in the words on the cards. (For example, **cats:** Can apples taste sour?)

5 The first player to finish each sentence gains a point.

6 Repeat until all cards have been used. The player with the most points at the end of the game wins.

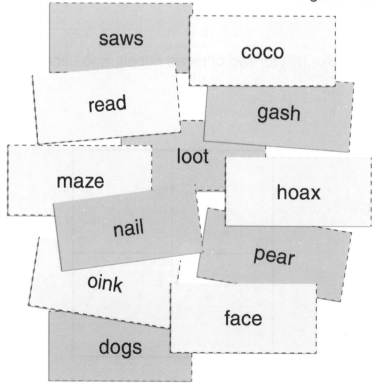

Week 9

This week, you can GET READY by:

- ◆ ordering adjectives
- ◆ figuring out the theme of a poem
- ◆ writing from different points of view
- ◆ using thumbprints to create art
- ◆ using scientific notation
- ◆ classifying triangles
- ◆ solving multistep word problems
- ◆ identifying similarities and differences in geography
- ◆ putting words into categories

Order of Adjectives

Directions: Adjectives have a specific order when written in sentences. Use the Order of Adjectives Chart to help you write sentences.

Order of Adjectives Chart
opinion
size
age
shape
color
origin
material
purpose

1 Write a sentence using three adjectives to describe a family member.

_____

_____

_____

2 Write a sentence using three adjectives to describe your favorite food.

_____

_____

_____

3 Write a sentence using three adjectives to describe an animal.

_____

_____

_____

4 Write a sentence using three adjectives to describe a game.

_____

_____

_____

What Is the Theme?

A *theme* is the central idea of a literary work. It is a lesson, moral, or message about life. Sometimes, the author clearly states the theme. More often, the author implies the theme. The reader must use clues from the text to figure it out.

Directions: Read the poem. Then, answer the questions.

Block City
by Robert Louis Stevenson

What are you able to build with your blocks?
Castles and palaces, temples and docks.
Rain may keep raining, and others go roam,
But I can be happy and building at home.

Let the sofa be mountains, the carpet be sea,
There I'll establish a city for me:
A kirk and a mill and a palace beside,
And a harbor as well where my vessels may ride.

Great is the palace with pillar and wall,
A sort of a tower on top of it all,
And steps coming down in an orderly way
To where my toy vessels lie safe in the bay.

This one is sailing and that one is moored:
Hark to the song of the sailors on board!
And see on the steps of my palace, the kings
Coming and going with presents and things!

1 What is the theme of this poem?

_____

_____

2 What lines in the poem helped you figure out the theme?

_____

_____

My Family from Different View Points

Directions: Write a paragraph about your family from a third-person point of view. Then, write a revised paragraph that shows a different point of view.

Thumbprint Pictures

Directions: Look at the thumbprints. What will these thumbprints become?
Create a drawing around each one.

Solve That Notation: Unknown Quantities

Scientific notation is a shorter way to write numbers. To convert numbers to scientific notation, place a decimal point after the first number. The exponent indicates how many places the decimal will move. Move positive exponent decimals to the right.

$10,000 = 1 \times 10^4$	$53,000 = 5.3 \times 10^4$
$1,000 = 1 \times 10^3$	$5,300 = 5.3 \times 10^3$
$100 = 1 \times 10^2$	$530 = 5.3 \times 10^2$
$10 = 1 \times 10^1$	$53 = 5.3 \times 10^1$
0	0

Directions: Write each number in scientific notation.

1 40,000

2 75,000

3 3,000

4 100,000

5 83

6 956

Directions: Write each number in standard form.

7 6×10^3

8 8×10^4

9 3×10^2

10 2.9×10^4

11 9.1×10^3

12 1.5×10^2

Triangles

A *triangle* is a two-dimensional polygon with three sides and three angles. You can classify triangles in two different ways.

Classify by Sides

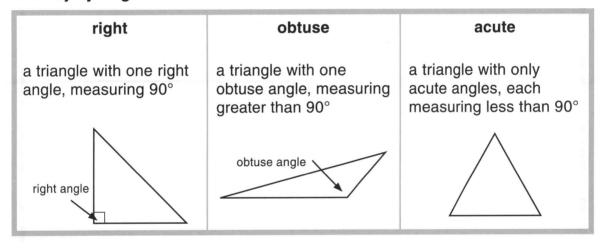

equilateral	isosceles	scalene
three equal sides; therefore, all sides are congruent	two equal sizes; therefore, two sides are congruent	no sides are equal; therefore, no sides are congruent

Classify by Angles

right	obtuse	acute
a triangle with one right angle, measuring 90°	a triangle with one obtuse angle, measuring greater than 90°	a triangle with only acute angles, each measuring less than 90°

right angle

obtuse angle

Directions: Classify each triangle by its sides and by its angles.

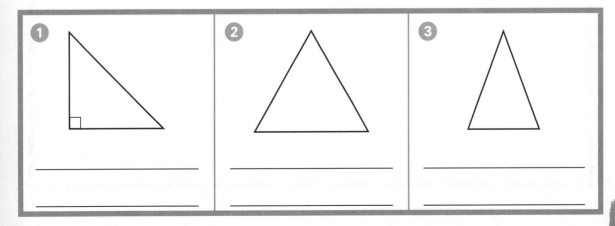

1.

2.

3.

Solve That Word Problem!

Directions: Read the word problems. You will need to do more than one step to solve each problem. Show the steps you take to find each final answer.

1 Renee enjoys building model cars as a hobby. She built 13 cars in June, 18 in July, and 23 in August. Then, she decided to give 16 to her brother. How many cars does Renee have left?

2 Ann did 30 jumping jacks in the morning and did 3 times that many in the afternoon. If she wants to do 120 jumping jacks in one day, how many will she need to do at night?

3 Two large pizzas have 24 slices total. If 7 friends want to share the pizzas, and they each want 3 slices, is there enough pizza? If so, how much is left?

What Doesn't Belong?

Directions: Each problem contains one place that does not belong. Find the one that does not belong. Then, explain your answer on the lines.

1 North America, Brazil, Canada, New York City

_____

_____

2 Asia, Himalayas, Germany, Ganges River

_____

_____

3 India, Africa, Europe, Australia, Antarctica

_____

_____

4 Indian Ocean, Andes Mountains, Gulf of Mexico, Mediterranean Sea, Red Sea

_____

_____

5 Tokyo, Los Angeles, Mexico, Vancouver

_____

_____

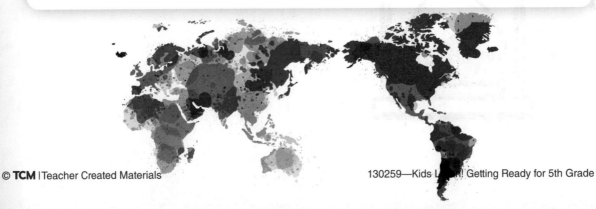

Categories

Number of Players

2–6

Materials

◆ *Category Cards* (page 111)

◆ *Letter Cards* (page 113)

◆ paper

◆ pens or pencils

◆ one-minute timer

Directions

1 Cut apart the *Category Cards* on page 111. Distribute one to each player or every two players.

2 Cut apart the *Letter Cards* on page 113. Shuffle and place them facedown in a pile.

3 Turn over a Letter Card. This card contains the letter you will use to begin a word for each category listed on the *Category Cards*.

4 Players will have one minute to come up with a word that begins with that letter for each category.

5 The first player to have a word for every category keeps that letter card.

6 Repeat until all cards have been used. The player with the most *Letter Cards* wins!

102 130259—Kids Learn! Getting Ready for 5th Grade

© **TCM** |Teacher Created Materials

Discussion Cards

Directions: Use these cards with the *Family Discussions* game on page 32.

If you could be any superhero, who would you be and why?	If you could invent anything, what would it be and how would it help people?
If you could meet anyone, past or present, who would it be and what would you ask that person?	What do you believe is the most important job? Why?
If you could be any animal, what would it be and why?	If you could be really good at something, what would it be and why?
If you could only eat the same meal every day for the rest of your life, what would it be and why?	What is the most important thing in the world? Why?

Family Discussions

Family Discussions

Family Discussions

Family Discussions

Family Discussions

Family Discussions

Family Discussions

Family Discussions

Math Problems Flashcards

Directions: Use these cards with the *Who Can Solve It?* game on page 52.

$108 \div 9 =$	$144 \div 6 =$
$243 \div 9 =$	$115 \div 5 =$
$267 \div 3 =$	$21 \times 17 =$
$56 \times 10 =$	$45 \times 43 =$
$12 \times 16 =$	$82 \times 34 =$

Who Can Solve It?　　　　　　　　Who Can Solve It?

Who Can Solve It?　　　　　　　　Who Can Solve It?

Who Can Solve It?　　　　　　　　Who Can Solve It?

Who Can Solve It?　　　　　　　　Who Can Solve It?

Who Can Solve It?　　　　　　　　Who Can Solve It?

Direction Cards

Directions: Use these cards with the *Toothpicks and Squares* game on page 62.

Take away four toothpicks to make only one square.

Take away two toothpicks to make three equal squares.

Take away one toothpick. Then, move four toothpicks to make 10 squares.

Take away two toothpicks to make two rectangles.

Move two toothpicks to make seven squares.

Toothpicks and Squares

Toothpicks and Squares

Toothpicks and Squares

Toothpicks and Squares

Toothpicks and Squares

Word Cards

Directions: Use these cards with the *Word Sentences* game on page 92.

coco	dogs
face	gash
hoax	loot
maze	nail
oink	pear
read	saws

Word Sentences

Word Sentences

Word Sentences

Word Sentences

Word Sentences

Word Sentences

Word Sentences

Word Sentences

Word Sentences

Word Sentences

Category Cards

Directions: Use these cards with the *Categories* game on page 102.

Categories

1. girl's name
2. sports team
3. science term
4. historical figure
5. item found at school

Categories

1. girl's name
2. sports team
3. science term
4. historical figure
5. item found at school

Categories

1. girl's name
2. sports team
3. science term
4. historical figure
5. item found at school

Categories

1. girl's name
2. sports team
3. science term
4. historical figure
5. item found at school

Categories

Categories

Categories

Categories

Letter Cards

Directions: Use these cards with the *Categories* game on page 102.

a	b	c
d	e	f
g	h	i
j	k	l
m	n	o
p	q	r
s	t	u
v	w	x
y	z	

Categories	Categories	Categories
Categories	Categories	Categories
Categories	Categories	Categories
Categories	Categories	Categories
Categories	Categories	Categories
Categories	Categories	Categories
Categories	Categories	Categories
Categories	Categories	Categories
	Categories	Categories

Preparing Your Child for Assessments

Background for Families

The Every Student Succeeds Act (ESSA) mandates that all states adopt challenging academic standards that help students meet the goal of college and career readiness. While many states already adopted academic standards prior to ESSA, the act continues to hold states accountable for detailed and comprehensive standards. Standards are designed to focus instruction and guide adoption of curricula. They define the knowledge, skills, and content students should acquire at each level. Standards are also used to develop standardized tests to evaluate students' academic progress.

Assessments are aligned with state standards. They typically include a variety of types of items. Some items ask students to select the correct option or options from a list. Other items ask students to give a written or numerical response. Students will also complete tasks that gauge their ability to bring together knowledge and skills across many standards.

Preparation Pages

The test preparation items on pages 116–127 provide sample test questions and tasks similar to those that may be found on standardized assessments. Use the following tips to work through the assessment practice pages with your child:

◆ Work with your child as they complete the practice items so that you can address any questions as they arise.

◆ Help your child understand how to go about selecting answers or working through tasks.

◆ Use the Answer Key to check the answers together, and discuss any incorrect responses.

◆ Keep in mind that for the purposes of this practice, getting the correct answer is not as important as helping your child become comfortable with the test-taking format and process.

Language Arts Assessment Practice

Directions: Read the passage. Then, answer the questions on page 117.

W. E. B. DuBois

W. E. B. DuBois was a Black writer and teacher. He wanted to change the way American society saw Black people.

He was born in Massachusetts in 1868. He was the first person in his family to go to high school. After that, he went to Fisk University and then Harvard University.

After finishing school, he taught at a university. There, he began a study in Philadelphia. He used data to analyze how people lived. DuBois said that the Black community's greatest challenges were poverty, crime, and lack of education. DuBois also did studies in the South. He learned that, even though slavery had ended decades before, it still affected how people lived.

DuBois and his family moved to Georgia. There he wrote his best-known book, *The Souls of Black Folk*. The book was a series of essays about the Black experience in America. DuBois's work inspired him to make the lives of Black people better. He became the director of the NAACP (National Association for the Advancement of Colored People). This organization seeks to improve the lives of Black people. He also edited their magazine.

In 1963, DuBois went to visit the African country of Ghana as part of research he was doing. He wanted to write an encyclopedia about the achievements of Black people. Sadly, DuBois became sick. He died in Ghana before it could be published.

Language Arts Assessment Practice *(cont.)*

1 Which of these best describes the text structure of the passage?

- Ⓐ chronology
- Ⓑ comparison
- Ⓒ cause and effect
- Ⓓ problem and solution

2 Write the numbers 1, 2, 3, and 4 to show the order of events in "W. E. B. DuBois."

☐ DuBois taught at the University of Pennsylvania.

☐ DuBois became director of the NAACP.

☐ DuBois wrote *The Souls of Black Folk*.

☐ DuBois attended Harvard University.

3 Where was DuBois working when he died?

- Ⓐ Georgia
- Ⓑ Philadelphia
- Ⓒ Ghana
- Ⓓ Massachusetts

Language Arts Assessment Practice *(cont.)*

Directions: Read the passage. Then, answer the questions on pages 118 and 119.

Afternoon on a Hill

by Edna St. Vincent Millay

I will be the gladdest thing
Under the sun!
I will touch a hundred flowers
And not pick one.

I will look at cliffs and clouds
With quiet eyes,
Watch the wind bow down the grass,
And the grass rise.

And when lights begin to show
Up from the town,
I will mark which must be mine,
And then start down!

---

4 What is a theme in "Afternoon on a Hill"?

Ⓐ Spending time with nature is a waste of time.

Ⓑ Spending time with nature can make you feel great.

Ⓒ Staying outside too long can have consequences.

Ⓓ Staying outside too long can be dangerous.

Language Arts Assessment Practice *(cont.)*

5 What does the author mean when she writes, "And when lights begin to show"?

(A) when the people leave their houses

(B) when she begins to dream

(C) when the house lights come on

(D) when the sun comes up in the morning

6 Which meaning of *bow* does the author mean in the line "Watch the wind bow down the grass"?

(A) a knot tied with two loops

(B) a weapon for shooting arrows

(C) a long stick used to play a violin

(D) a forward bend

7 Read the sentence. What is the meaning of "it cost an arm and a leg"?

Amal wanted a new video game, but it cost an arm and a leg.

(A) It was expensive.

(B) It was cheap.

(C) It was easy to find.

(D) It was not available.

Language Arts Assessment Practice (cont.)

8 In the sentences, underline words that should be capitalized, and add any necessary punctuation.

Ⓐ bari said her favorite author is jane austen

Ⓑ jorge lives on franklin street

Ⓒ toni likes to jog in timber park mountain park and by lake meade

Ⓓ will you go to the san diego zoo with abdul and kelly

9 Write *your* or *you're* to complete each sentence.

Ⓐ Where is _____ jacket?

Ⓑ I think _____ a good friend.

Ⓒ When _____ ready, go ahead.

Ⓓ She said that _____ dog is cute.

Language Arts Assessment Practice *(cont.)*

10 Which pronoun best completes the sentence?

Dad wanted to know _____ broke the window.

(A) that

(B) which

(C) who

(D) where

11 Read the sentence. What part of speech is the word *loudly*?

Tasha cheered loudly when she got an A.

(A) noun

(B) adjective

(C) verb

(D) adverb

12 Correct the run-on sentence by rewriting it as two sentences.

Raf was excited as he packed they were leaving tomorrow for vacation.

_____

_____

_____

Language Arts Assessment Practice *(cont.)*

13 Write a set of instructions explaining how to do something you know well. If you need anything to complete the task, include a list of materials.

_____

_____

_____

_____

_____

_____

_____

_____

_____

_____

_____

_____

_____

_____

_____

_____

Math Assessment Practice

1 Bella played a game on her phone. She scored 346 points on one level, 481 points on the next level, and 259 on the third level. About how many points did she score in all? (Round to the nearest hundred.)

_____

2 Write how much time has passed in hours and minutes.

Ⓐ from 7 a.m. to 2:30 p.m.   _____

Ⓑ from 11 a.m. to 4:45 p.m.   _____

Ⓒ from 9:30 a.m. to 11:45 a.m.   _____

Ⓓ from 10:45 a.m. to 4:40 p.m.   _____

3 Compare the numbers using <, >, or =.

Ⓐ 64,811 ◯ 68,432

Ⓑ 118,671 ◯ 112,549

Ⓒ 306,121 ◯ 306,582

Ⓓ 456,785 ◯ 456,795

Math Assessment Practice *(cont.)*

④ Round each decimal to the nearest whole number.

Ⓐ 782.75 _____

Ⓑ 89.35 _____

Ⓒ 16.66 _____

Ⓓ 452.42 _____

⑤ A rug is 8 feet long and 6 feet wide. What is the area of the rug?

_____

⑥ Gregory grows tomatoes in his garden. He picks 14 on Tuesday, 28 on Wednesday, and 6 on Thursday. Then, he gives 12 tomatoes to his aunt. How many tomatoes does he have left?

_____

Math Assessment Practice (cont.)

7 Ms. Chen's class gathered leaves outside. Then, they measured the leaves. They recorded the lengths of the leaves, in inches, in a line plot.

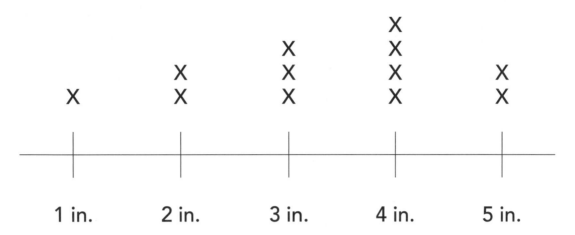

(A) What is the most common length of the leaves? _____

(B) What is the length of the longest leaf? _____

8 What is the quotient? Write your answer as a whole number with a remainder.

268 ÷ 14

Math Assessment Practice (cont.)

9 Which fractions are equivalent to $\frac{3}{5}$? Select 3 correct answers.

(A) $\frac{6}{10}$

(B) $\frac{3}{10}$

(C) $\frac{9}{15}$

(D) $\frac{12}{20}$

(E) $\frac{16}{20}$

10 What is the product?

$$\begin{array}{r} 35 \\ \times\ 63 \\ \hline \end{array}$$

11 What is the sum?

$$\frac{5}{8} + \frac{3}{4}$$

Math Assessment Practice *(cont.)*

12 A shop sells apples at a cost of $2 per pound. What is the cost of 5 pounds of apples?

_____

13 Which term best describes each triangle shown? Write *acute*, *obtuse*, or *right*.

Ⓐ   _____

Ⓑ   _____

Ⓒ   _____

Answer Key

Week 1

It's All Relative! (page 14)

1. that
2. who
3. whose
4. which
5. whom
6. which

A Visit with Penguins (page 15)

1. Check that sentence(s) include some of the main ideas of the passage.
2. Check that response includes a prediction and a reason to support it.

Circus Balloon (page 16)

Check that written response includes descriptive words and details.

T-Shirt Designer (page 17)

Check that the T-shirt design is for a charity.

Raffle Tickets (page 18)

1. 6,942; six thousand, nine hundred forty-two
2. 10,753; ten thousand, seven hundred fifty-three
3. 24,197; twenty-four thousand, one hundred ninety-seven
4. 40,735; forty thousand, seven hundred thirty-five
5. 61,217; sixty-one thousand, two hundred seventeen
6. 81,369; eighty-one thousand, three hundred sixty-nine
7. 6,194; six thousand, one hundred ninety-four
8. 16,591; sixteen thousand, five hundred ninety-one
9. 84,894; eighty-four thousand, eight hundred ninety-four

Calculating Area (page 19)

1. 15 ft.^{2}
2. 2,322 cm^2
3. 1,250 m^2
4. 108 ft.^{2}

Solving by Estimating (page 20)

1. 10 cats
2. 30 boxes
3. 1,700 points

Which Explorer Went Where? (page 21)

Francisco Pizarro—Conquered the Incas

Ferdinand Magellan—The first to travel around the world

Christopher Columbus—Sailed with the *Niña*, *Pinta*, and *Santa Maria*

Hernán Cortés—Caused the fall of the Aztec empire

Roll-the-Numbers Multiplication Game (page 22)

Check that multiplication is done correctly.

Week 2

Sentence Emergencies (page 24)

1. **The** students in **Mr. Garcia's** class were reading **Charlotte's Web.**
2. **What** a wonderful day it is**!**
3. **Jordan,** come play with us in **Griffith Park.**
4. **Watch** out, **Michelle!**

Reading a Shake Recipe (page 25)

1. C
2. D

Read All About It! (page 26)

Check that newspaper article contains the *who, what, when, where, why,* and *how.*

Hollywood Star (page 27)

Check that the flyer describes the movie with pictures and words.

Answer Key *(cont.)*

Express This Number *(page 28)*

1. thirty-four thousand, two hundred sixty-two; 30,000 + 4,000 + 200 + 60 + 2

2. seven hundred eighty-one thousand, four hundred fifteen; 700,000 + 80,000 + 1,000 + 400 + 10 + 5

3. 51,527; 50,000 + 1,000 + 500 + 20 + 7

4. 923,334; 900,000 + 20,000 + 3,000 + 300 + 30 + 4

5. 23,469; twenty-three thousand, four hundred sixty-nine

Line Them Up: Making Line Plots *(page 29)*

1.

```
              x           x
      x       x   x   x   x           x
  x   x   x   x   x   x   x   x
  1   1¼  1¾   2   2½  2¾  3¼  3½
  in. in. in. in. in. in. in. in.
```

2. $1\frac{3}{4}$ inches and $2\frac{1}{2}$ inches
3. $3\frac{1}{2}$ inches
4. 1 inch
5. $2\frac{1}{2}$ inches

Multistep Word Problems *(page 30)*

1. 47 stamps
2. 11 strawberries
3. Yes; $0.25

Many Ways to Say 10 *(page 31)*

20 ÷ 2	8 + 2	10 x 1	20 x .5	100 ÷ 10	15 – 5
15 – 5	20 x .5	100 ÷ 10	8 + 2	10 x 1	20 ÷ 2
100 ÷ 10	15 – 5	20 x .5	20 ÷ 2	8 + 2	10 x 1
8 + 2	10 x 1	20 ÷ 2	100 ÷ 10	15 – 5	20 x .5
20 x .5	100 ÷ 10	15 – 5	10 x 1	20 ÷ 2	8 + 2
10 x 1	20 ÷ 2	8 + 2	15 – 5	20 x .5	100 ÷ 10

Family Discussions *(page 32)*

Check that responses are not repeated and each person discusses the similarities and differences between responses.

Week 3

Stop That Sentence! *(page 34)*

1. My books are on the table. My math book is on top.

2. They were closing the store. It was time to go home.

3. Watch out for the slippery ice. You could fall and hurt yourself.

4. I got a new blue shirt. My blue shoes match perfectly.

5. My brother made the team. Will I be able to play baseball someday?

It's a Matter of Opinion *(page 35)*

The opinion sentence is *Everybody needs to have a pet.* Answer may include: The author supports the opinion with reasons and evidence about the benefits of pets that will convince the reader to believe that everyone needs one.

You're a Star! *(page 36)*

Check that the story explains how and why he or she became famous and other important things he or she might do in the future.

The Most Outrageous Dog Park *(page 37)*

Check that the symbols on the legend are clearly marked on the diagram.

Let's Compare! *(page 38)*

1. 65,812 < 79,458
2. 512,327 > 87,959
3. 672,735 < 673,736
4. 783,583 = 783,583
5. 23,428 < 32,482
6. 521,708 > 512,945
7. 834,499 = 834,499
8. 107,368 < 392,010

Answer Key *(cont.)*

Making Equivalent Fractions (page 39)

The following are some example answers:

1. $\frac{2}{3} = \frac{6}{9} = \frac{18}{27}$
2. $\frac{3}{8} = \frac{6}{16} = \frac{12}{32}$
3. $\frac{4}{5} = \frac{16}{20} = \frac{64}{80}$
4. $\frac{9}{10} = \frac{27}{30} = \frac{81}{90}$
5. $\frac{8}{13} = \frac{16}{26} = \frac{32}{52}$

Fraction Word Problems (page 40)

1. They ate $\frac{3}{4}$ of a pizza.
2. He made $\frac{4}{10}$ or $\frac{2}{5}$ of his shots.
3. She used 15 eggs.

Dinner Table Seating Chart (page 41)

George Washington	Benjamin Franklin	James Madison
Thomas Jefferson	John Adams	Alexander Hamilton

There may be other solutions. Check that the placement of the names represent the clues.

The Tallest Paper Tower (page 42)

Check that each player answers the discussion questions.

Week 4

To, Too, or Two? (page 44)

1. I'm going **to** be in a dance recital tomorrow. I'll be wearing my new tutu, which is a little **too** big. **Two** of my friends will dance, **too**. I'm **too** excited **to** sleep, but I have **to** go **to** bed.

2. The leaves were falling from the trees as I walked **to** school. It must be fall, which I call autumn, **too**. I know that there are **two** more weeks until Halloween. I can't wait **to** go trick-or-treating! My friend Alexa is going **to** walk with me, **too**. We will remember **to** say "Thank you!" after we get our candy. I hope that I get at least **two** lollipops **to** eat!

An Author's Use of Evidence (page 45)

The following are example answers:

1. The author uses such evidence as "Over an hour passed before we were seated, and no one apologized for this inconvenience" and " The server was quite rude when we asked for the items that we ordered."

2. The restaurant manager will likely change his actions since the customer made it clear that he wants to be a loyal customer but would like to see improvements. The restaurant manager will assume other customers feel this way, and the restaurant may lose business if it continues in this fashion.

Letter to the Mayor (page 46)

Check that response includes a proper opening and closing for a letter.

Room Designer Extraordinaire! (page 47)

Check that the room includes pictures for each category.

Rounding Decimals (page 48)

1. 51
2. 96
3. 21
4. 5.9
5. 13.7
6. 45.3
7. 3.91
8. 851.43
9. 0.63
10. Answer may include: *Because there is no denomination for $0.001, and $0.01 is the smallest denomination, so you must round to the nearest hundredth when dealing with money.*

Match the Fraction (page 49)

1. C
2. D
3. F
4. A
5. E
6. B

Answer Key *(cont.)*

Real World Fractions (page 50)

1. $12 \times \frac{3}{4} = \frac{36}{4} = 9$ pencils
2. $24 \times \frac{1}{3} = \frac{24}{3} = 8$ cupcakes
3. $18 \times \frac{2}{3} = \frac{36}{3} = 12$; $18 - 12 = 6$ balls

Connect the Dots (page 51)

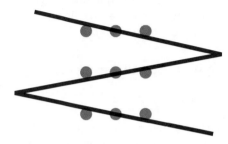

Check that responses describe how the puzzle was solved and how many tries were attempted.

Who Can Solve It? (page 52)

$108 \div 9 = 12$	$21 \times 17 = 357$
$144 \div 6 = 24$	$56 \times 10 = 560$
$243 \div 9 = 27$	$45 \times 43 = 1935$
$115 \div 5 = 23$	$12 \times 16 = 192$
$267 \div 3 = 89$	$82 \times 34 = 2788$

Week 5

Adjectives and Adverbs (page 54)

The following are example answers:

1. The small dog barked rapidly at the large, lazy cat.
2. I somehow hit the speeding ball hastily.
3. Mei Ling ravenously ate lunch.
4. Everyone enthusiastically watched Rafael energetically play basketball.

Inferring from a Picture (page 55)

The following are example answers:

1. The animals might be introducing or getting to know each other. The animals look curious.
2. They are facing each other so that they can check each other out.

It's Alive! (page 56)

Check that the response includes facts and details about the chosen domain and that information was found from credible sources.

True Identity (page 57)

Check that the face has features added to reveal a person's identity.

Multiply Using a Standard Algorithm (page 58)

1. row 1: 92; row 2: 1,380; row 3: 1,472
2. row 1: 459; row 2: 3,060; row 3: 3,519
3. row 1: 100; row 2: 2,000; row 3: 2,100
4. row 1: 564; row 2: 940; row 3: 1,504
5. 192 notebooks and 288 folders

Turning a Fraction into a Decimal (page 59)

1. 0.5
2. 0.9
3. 0.2
4. 0.07
5. 0.04
6. 0.26
7. 0.08
8. 0.4
9. 0.06
10. 0.98

Answer Key *(cont.)*

Features of Shapes (page 60)

1. right triangle

2. rectangle

3. trapezoid

4. parallelogram

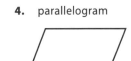

5. acute triangle

6. square

Awesome Analogies (page 61)

1. pig : oink :: dog : bark

2. duck : quack :: cow : moo

3. fish : swim :: cheetah : run

4. today : tomorrow :: yesterday : today

5. gray : black :: pink : red

Check that analogies are written correctly.

Toothpicks and Squares (page 62)

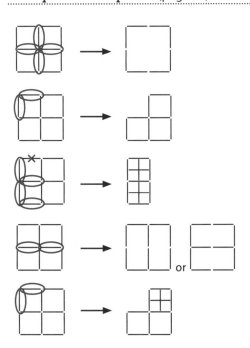

Week 6

Put Them in Order (page 64)

The sequence of the sentences should be as follows:

I woke up one morning . . . I got out of bed . . . What a shock I got when . . . I ran to my mother . . . She said, "It appears that those seeds . . ." Then she looked . . . I am feeling better now . . .

Identifying Text Structure (page 65)

Text structure: Chronology

Evidence: The text includes events or steps in order of how they happen. The text contains such signal words as *First*, *Next*, and *Then*.

Movie Review (page 66)

Check that review includes details about the plot, descriptions of the characters, and details to support the main idea.

There's a Hole in My Paper (page 67)

Check that the picture includes the hole.

What's Remaining? (page 68)

1. 1 R1

2. 4 R3

3. 16

4. 21 R3

5. 14 R4

6. 7 R1

7. 108

8. 14 R1

9. 25

Answer Key (cont.)

Getting Decimals in Line (page 69)

1. 0.9, 0.5, 0.07, 0.06
2. 0.9, 0.061, 0.06, 0.04
3. 0.8, 0.4, 0.12, 0.002
4. 0.9, 0.57, 0.09, 0.006

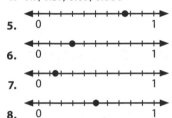

5. (number line 0 to 1)
6. (number line 0 to 1)
7. (number line 0 to 1)
8. (number line 0 to 1)

Fraction Party Riddles (page 70)

1. 10 pounds of ribs
2. $7\frac{1}{5}$ pounds of salmon
3. 4 pies

What Happened? (page 71)

Jack is a fish, and his tank has broken. He landed in the boot on the floor next to the table. Water and glass from the tank surround the boot on the floor.

Your child is the driver, so the eye color of the driver is whatever color he or she has.

Move Those Things! (page 72)

Check that players do not touch the items with their hands and that each utensil is used one time.

Week 7

Clue Me In! (page 74)

Clue: never found on its own

Definition: removed by pulling or cutting out

Clue: just about everywhere

Definition: large amount of something

A Letter of Despair (page 75)

Multiple parts may be underlined. Some examples include: *I have never imagined such horror as I have seen these last few days at Shiloh; The first day of fighting was a clear Southern victory; I lived through the bloodiest day of the war thus far; General Johnston himself was slain by a cannon blast, and General Beauregard took over command; Our own dear friends, Kurt Flanders and Willem Simpson, fell; My heart grieves for them and for their families back home in Georgia; General Buell arrived with Grant's reinforcements; In the end, General Beauregard was forced to withdraw our troops back to Corinth. Comments in the margin should reflect the child's feelings.*

That's Funny! (page 76)

Check that response is about a funny or embarrassing moment.

What's Does It Look Like? (page 77)

Check that the steps are detailed.

Get the Message! (page 78)

T	37 R12	**U**	284	**D**	92 R1
A	150	**J**	152 R18	**N**	304 R5
G	237 R3	**B**	1,242 R4	**O**	19
W	73 R3	**E**	25	**Y**	22 R2
V	15 R3	**H**	33 R6	**R**	8 R3

Message: Whatever you are, be a good one.

Accurate Areas (page 79)

1. 15 cm^2
2. 12 cm^2
3. 16 cm^2
4. 30 cm^2
5. 180 cm^2
6. 30 cm^2
7. 16 cm^2
8. 36 cm^2

Answer Key *(cont.)*

How Long Does It Take? (page 80)

1. A. 7 hours, 20 minutes; B. 3 hours, 50 minutes; C. 4 hours, 35 minutes; D. 1 hour, 5 minutes; E. 5 hours, 45 minutes; F. 4 hours, 15 minutes
2. 2 hours, 15 minutes
3. 12:52 P.M.
4. 10:20 A.M.
5. A. 375 minutes; B. 6 hours, 15 minutes

Who Is Responsible for What? (page 81)

1. Susan B. Anthony
2. Lewis and Clark
3. Martin Luther King Jr.
4. James Madison
5. Benjamin Franklin
6. Teddy Roosevelt

Dough Boats (page 82)

Make sure that the winning boat stays afloat. Be sure to answer the discussion questions.

Week 8

Idioms (page 84)

The following are example answers:

1. She meant that the movie was amazing.
2. He meant that his father would not stand for it any longer.
3. She meant that she would be leaving.
4. He meant that he was not feeling well.
5. He meant that he slept very deeply.

The Crazier the Better (page 85)

1. José likes Crazy Hair Day because he "loved being goofy, and he loved making his classmates laugh." Crazy Hair Day lets José do both of those things.
2. In third grade, José "braided his hair into 16 tiny braids." Then, he "wrapped a pipe cleaner around each braid and stuck paper airplanes to the ends" and called the design Fly Boy.
3. José is planning to use the bird's nest for Crazy Hair Day. "It was going to be the perfect Crazy Hair Day accessory!"

Here's How You Do It! (page 86)

Check that response is in correct step-by-step order.

The Most Amazing Machine (page 87)

Check that the picture and notes describe the machine.

Looking for a Pattern Problems (page 88)

Problem A

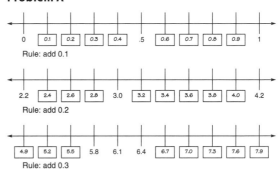

Problem B

Check that the number line and rule match.

Target Number (page 89)

The following are example answers:

1. $1 + 2 = 3$; $(4 - 3) \times 3 = 3$; $(4 + 2) \div 2 = 3$
2. $8 - 6 = 2$; $10 - 8 = 2$; $(7 + 9) \div 8 = 2$; $(7 + 9) - (6 + 8) = 2$
3. $3 + 3 + 6 = 12$; $5 \times 3 - 3 = 12$; $(6 \times 3) - (3 + 3) = 12$
4. $(5 \times 10) \div 10 = 5$; $(4 \times 10) \div (4 + 4) = 5$; $10 - 5 = 5$

Consumer Math (page 90)

1. $10.38
2. No, she will be under by $1.95.
3. $13.83
4. 36 cups

Answer Key *(cont.)*

Eye Color (page 91)

1. They have a 50-50 chance of having a child with blue eyes and having a child with brown eyes.

2.

	B	b
B	BB	Bb
b	Bb	bb

Word Sentences (page 92)

Check that each letter in the words on the cards is used in the sentence.

Week 9

Order of Adjectives (page 94)

The following are example answers:

1. My dad is funny, thin, and tan.
2. Pizza is delicious, round, and cheesy.
3. Dogs are intelligent, furry, and companionable.
4. Football is exciting, intense, and entertaining.

What Is the Theme? (page 95)

The following are example answers:

1. The theme of the poem is that anything is possible when you use your imagination.
2. The author uses lines such as "But I can be happy building at home. / Let the sofa be mountains, the carpet be sea" to let readers know the theme is imagination.

My Family from Different View Points (page 96)

Check that both responses are written from another person's point of view.

Thumbprint Pictures (page 97)

Check that the pictures are drawn around the thumbprints.

Solve That Notation: Unknown Quantities (page 98)

1. 4×10^4
2. 7.5×10^4
3. 3×10^3
4. 1×10^5
5. 8.3×10^1
6. 9.56×10^2
7. 6,000
8. 80,000
9. 300
10. 29,000
11. 9,100
12. 150

Triangles (page 99)

1. isosceles; right
2. equilateral; acute
3. isosceles; acute

Solve That Word Problem! (page 100)

1. 38 cars
2. 0 jumping jacks
3. Yes; 3 slices are left.

What Doesn't Belong? (page 101)

1. Brazil does not belong because it is in South America and the other places are all in North America.
2. Germany does not belong because it is not in Asia like the other places.
3. India does not belong because it is a country and not a continent.
4. The Andes Mountains does not belong because it is a mountain range and the other places are bodies of water.
5. Mexico does not belong because it is a country and the other things listed are all cities in the world.

Categories (page 102)

Check that players use the correct letter for each category.

Language Arts Assessment Practice (pages 116 - 122)

1. A
2. 2, 4, 3, 1
3. C
4. B
5. C

Answer Key *(cont.)*

6. D

7. A

8. A. <u>Bari</u> said her favorite author is <u>Jane Austen</u>.
   B. <u>Jorge</u> lives on <u>Franklin Street</u>.
   C. <u>Toni</u> likes to jog in <u>Timber Park</u>, <u>Mountain Park</u>, and by <u>Lake Meade</u>.
   D. <u>Will</u> you go to the <u>San Diego Zoo</u> with <u>Abdul</u> and <u>Kelly</u>?

9. A. your, B. you're, C. you're, D. your

10. C

11. D

12. Example: Raf was excited as he packed. They were leaving for vacation tomorrow.

13. Responses should include steps and any materials needed.

Math Assessment Practice

(pages 123-127)

1. 1,100 points

2. A. 7 hours and 30 minutes
   B. 5 hours and 45 minutes
   C. 2 hours and 15 minutes
   D. 5 hours and 55 minutes

3. A. < B. > C. < D. <

4. A. 783, B. 89, C. 17, D. 452

5. 48 square feet

6. 36 tomatoes

7. A. 4 inches, B. 5 inches

8. 19 R2

9. A, C, D

10. 2,205

11. $1\frac{3}{8}$

12. $10

13. A. right, B. obtuse, C. acute

© **TCM** | Teacher Created Materials

130259—Kids Learn! Getting Ready for 5th Grade

139

© **TCM** | Teacher Created Materials

130259—Kids Learn! Getting Ready for 5th Grade

141

_____   _____
_____   _____
_____   _____
_____   _____
_____   _____

© **TCM** | Teacher Created Materials

130259—Kids Learn! Getting Ready for 5th Grade

143